This book is dedicated to

Love

We Are Love

Written and illustrated
by
Jennifer Black

What is love?   Where is it from?

What does it look like?   Can I have some?

Will I find it in the garden?   Will I find it in the sky?

Will I find it in my house?   Will I find it if I try?

Yes! You will find it in the garden.
You will find it in the sky.

You will find it in your house.
You will find it if you try.

Love is the power of the universe.
It shines through every star.

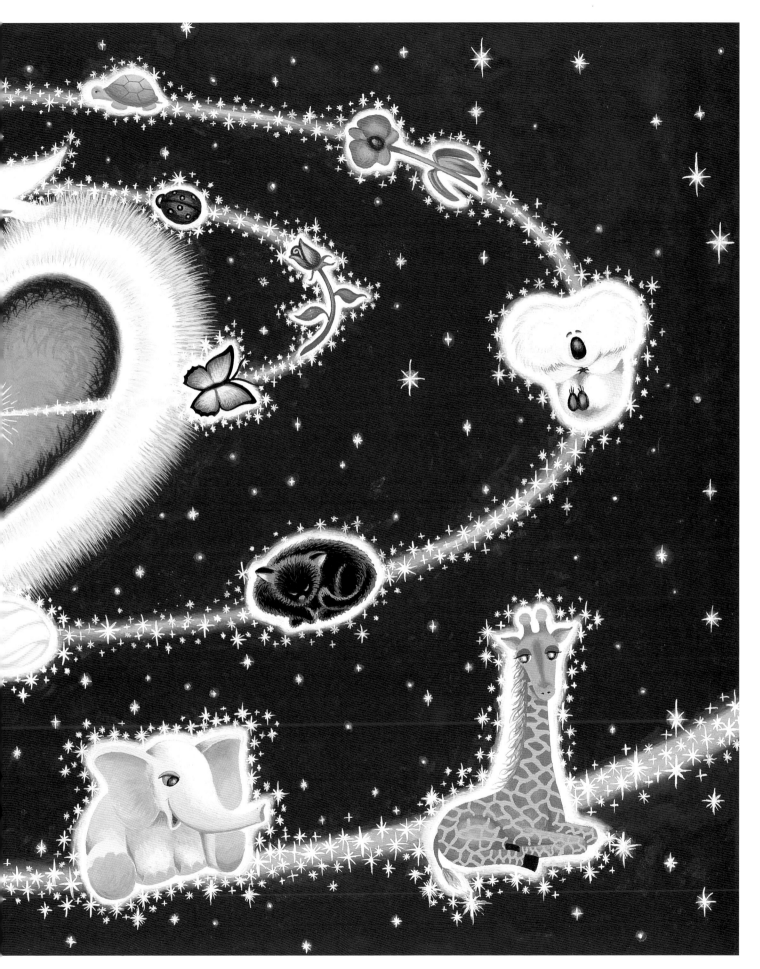

Love lights up everything you see.
Love is who You are.

Love colors our world in rainbows of light

and makes all the flowers bloom.

Love rests in the quiet stillness of night

by the light of the silvery moon.

You can see it in the rising sun
that greets each brand new day.

Love shines its light for us to grow,
to sing and dance and play.

You can hear it in the whistling wind
and when the raindrops fall.

You can hear love in your laughter,
sharing joy with one and all.

You can feel it when you plant a tree

and tend the land with care.

You can feel it when you swim the sea,

or sit in silent prayer.

You can see it shine in loving eyes
and a smile full of grace,

or watching a baby and its mother
sharing a sweet embrace.

You will know it when your heart feels warm
and your face begins to glow.

Love is how you bless yourself
and everyone you know.

Love is the power of the universe.
It shines through every star.

Love lights up everything you see.
Love is who You are.

It grows from deep within your heart
and shows you how to care,

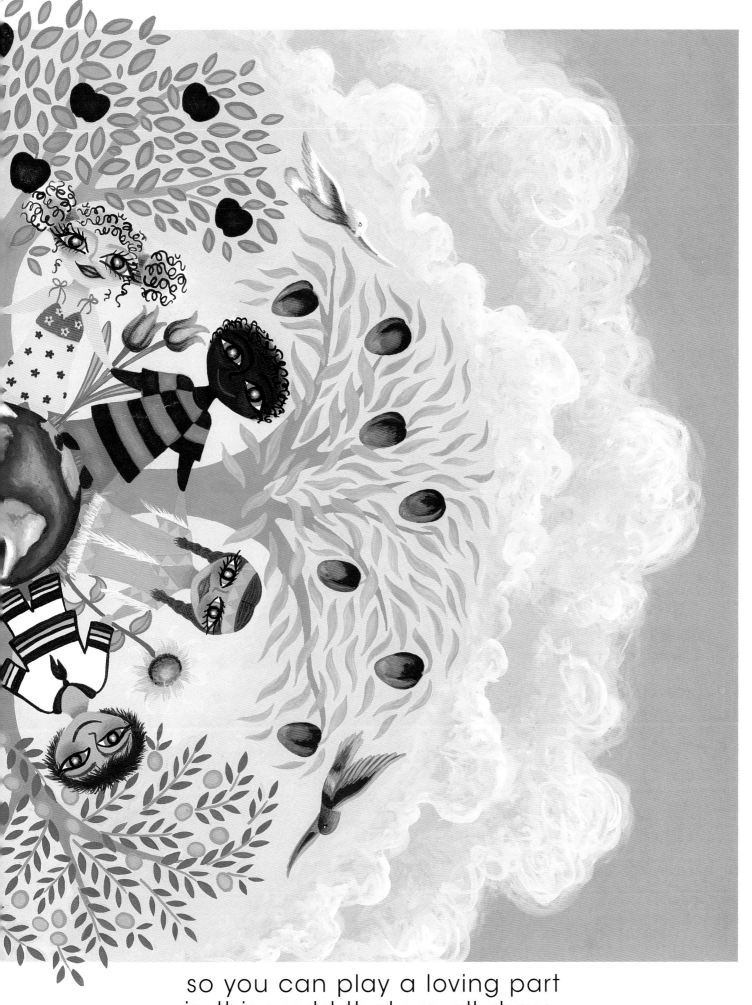

so you can play a loving part
in this world that we all share.

So share all your love with family and friends,
with the plants and animals too.

Then you will know that love never ends...
Love will always be me and you.

The World of
We Are One

The World of We Are One is devoted to sharing messages
of unity and love that inspire us to honor and appreciate each other.

Our initial offerings come in the form of children's picture books, *We Are Love* and We Are One.

We Are One is a rhythmic poem accompanied by vibrant illustrations
that speaks to children and to the child within us all of unity. It is a gentle
reminder that no matter what our nationality, gender, faith, species, shape,
size, color, or that we make different sounds and see things individually, we
are all essentially the same.

'We are all one but different. Different but the same.
Created by the one light, we are each given a name.'

To delve deeper into the virtues that support unity, compassion
and love, two sets of interactive cards have been created
We Are Love ♥ Journey of the Heart Cards
We Are One Exploration Cards

The World of We Are One intends to include various other mediums, such as music, visual arts,
interactive educational programs, DVD and multi media using a variety of like minded artisans.
For these products and more, please visit:
www.worldofweareone.com

ILLUMINATION Arts

Published by Illumination Arts LLC,
140 Adams St, Quincy, MA 02169
info@illuminationarts.us   www.illuminationarts.us
Library of Congress Cataloging - in - publication Data
Library of Congress Control Number: 2010911713
We Are Love / written and illustrated by Jennifer Black
Summary: We Are Love is a children's picture book that explores the source
of love and shares how it can be experienced in our daily lives.
ISBN 9-7809829225-1-4 (hardcover)
Published in the United States of America
Printed in China by Shanghai Kangshi Printing Co.,Ltd
Image Reproduction/Colour Management Clayton Lloyd - Flawless Imaging
Layout/Pre-press Vanessa Szychter - OpenArt Design

There are
65 hearts within the
'story pages' of this book.

Can you find
them all?